Daphne Kitching writes and performs poetry for children and has had her work published in anthologies by several publishers including: *The Way Through the Woods* and *The Mighty Ark* (Oxford University Press), *Football Fever* (Oxford University Press), *I'm In a Mood Today* (Oxford University Press), *Whizz Bang Orang Utan* (Oxford University Press) and *Minibeasts* (Macmillan).

She has had a Christmas play published in a collection by Scripture Union *Maximus Mouse's Christmas Card and other Christmas plays*, and has written short stories to improve auditory attention.

Daphne teaches pupils with Specific Learning Difficulties (Dyslexia) and has many years experience as a primary school teacher in North Yorkshire.

She is a member of The National Association of Writers in Education.

Daphne was born in Scholes, Cleckheaton and now lives in East Yorkshire with her husband David. They have three children - James, John and Hannah.

Tod Leedale was born in Bradford, spent his childhood abroad and decided on a career in art and graphics because he could 'draw a bit'. He describes himself as a children's illustrator because that is mainly what he does and what he enjoys most. He has illustrated a number of books including *Brilliant!* (Kingston Press). Tod lives in Lincolnshire and currently works from home producing graphics for an educational software company.

"While there are some good poems which are only for adults — there are no good poems which are only for children."

WH Auden

AS LONG AS
THERE ARE TREES

A selection of poems
by Daphne Kitching

Illustrations by Tod Leedale

For Marjorie and Julian,
with my love,
Daphne
x x June 2002

Kingston
Press

British Library Cataloguing in Publication Data.
A catalogue record for this book is available from the British Library.

First published 2001

All poems © 2001 Daphne Kitching
All illustrations © 2001 Tod Leedale

Published by Kingston Press

ISBN 1 902039 10 6

Kingston Press is the publishing imprint of Kingston upon Hull City Libraries, Central Library, Albion Street, Kingston upon Hull, England HU1 3TF
Telephone: +44 (0) 1482 616814
Fax: +44 (0) 1482 616827
E-mail: kingstonpress@hullcc.demon.co.uk
Internet: www.hullcc.gov.uk/kingstonpress

Printed by Kingston upon Hull City Council Printing Services, 35 Witham, Kingston upon Hull, England HU9 1DA.

CONTENTS

As long as there are ... Monsters, Mysteries and Make-believe

As long as there are ... Feelings

As long as there is ... School

As long as there are ... Trees (and other interesting things)

As long as there are ... Families

As long as there are ... Animals

As long as there is ... Word Play

As long as there are ... Seasons

**As long as there are ...
Monsters, Mysteries and Make-believe**

THE MANY-FOOTED-MONSTER

In our house,
But we don't know where,
Lives a Many-footed-monster
Whose many feet are bare.
No-one's ever seen him,
He's as clever as a fox,
But we know that he's been prowling
When we try to find our socks.

The Many-footed-monster
Steals our socks to warm his feet,
And those he doesn't need to wear
We think he likes to eat.
The Many-footed-monster
Has the strangest kind of taste,
He doesn't like his socks to match
Which seems like *such* a waste.

One red, one blue, one striped, one checked,
One long, one short, one mended,
One for him and one for us,
One peaceful morning ended.
The Many-footed-monster
Takes our socks and hides away,
He doesn't care how strange *we* look
With mixed up feet next day!

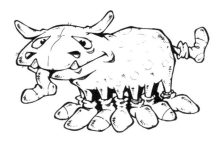

DUVETSAURUS FEATHERFILL.

The world at night belongs to me
As I close my bedroom door.
I lie awake and wait for him,
My secret dinosaur!
Duvetsaurus Featherfill
Who no-one else has found.
I met him first one sleepless night
As he was prowling round
And round my bunk bed,
Feeling restless, just like me.
As I tossed and wriggled
Duvetsaurus copied me.

We have some great adventures,
He changes shape each night,
From long and flat while sleeping,
To tall and fat, to fight!
Not only can his shape change,
But his pattern can as well.
Every week, on washday,
(Just as he begins to smell)
He cleverly transforms himself
To blend in with my bed,
So no-one ever knows he's there,
But him and me……..and Ted.

METAMORPHOSIS

A Year Three boy that I once knew
Whose name was Henry Miller,
Ignored the warnings, given in love,
From wise Great-Aunt Camilla,
(And Mrs Snap his teacher,
And his brothers Sam and Jude)
Of what would surely happen
If he continually chewed.

Henry chewed through reading books
Whilst other children read.
He chewed the wood from pencils
Leaving piles of useless lead.
He chewed through plastic counting bricks
Designed to aid subtraction,
And joining bits from jigsaws
With a curious, zigzag action.

From waking in the morning,
And no matter what his mood,
Till his head sank on his pillows
Henry chewed and chewed and chewed.
A trail of Hen-destruction
Could be followed every day.
Shredded paper, wood and toys,
A childhood chewed away.

The warnings Aunt Camilla gave
Of chew-related dangers,
Became reality one day
As people noticed changes.
A metamorphosis occurred
In compulsive Henry Miller,
He now lives in a jam jar —
A Year Three caterpillar!

CLOUD CLOTHES

The mountain is a monster
With moods good and bad.
You can tell by the clouds he dresses in
What kind of day he's had.

On angry, "Hate you," steer-clear days
He wears purple, grey and black,
Thick dark hoods and veils and wigs
Disguise the shape of his back.

He rumbles or bellows his discontent,
He lashes with whips of rain,
When the mountain puts on his bad mood clouds
Stay away till he's peaceful again!

Blue and white with streaks of gold
Is his choice when he's feeling good,
They show off his wonderful velvet coat
And sing out of his gentle mood.

He beckons his friends to share with him
The views of the world from on high,
To clamber and marvel and rest on him
As they reach his face in the sky.

But remember to watch for his change of clothes,
Be ready to pack up and leave,
For the purple and black that he wears on his head
Can quickly come down to his sleeve.

WONDERING IF THEY'RE WONDERING

Are there people in space, outside the world,
Do they dream of the planets they see?

Do they ever look up and wonder
If there could be such a person as me?

Do they study the earth and send rockets,
Do their people explore while we sleep?

Shall we one day wake up to invaders from space
Who keep trying to talk but just bleep?

Are there people in space I keep asking,
Do they gaze and pretend just like me?

Or do they believe that nothing could live
On the blue earth they so long to see?

LIFE IN ALIEN NATION

Alien and Alienesse
Have a beautiful alienome,
Where they live with their alienildren
And their bright red aliengnome.

He is an alienologist
At the Alienfirmary,
Finding cures for alienitis
In the local community.

Alienache is common,
Alienella is rare
But is spread by disease in alien eggs,
So owners take note – and BEWARE!

She is an alienobat,
Every morning she swings and she climbs.
Then after lunch she's an alienmum
Reading alienursery rhymes.

They speak in Alienanish,
They travel by alienar,
Their life in Alien Nation
Is alieneally bizarre!

EPITAPH TO A VICTIM OF DESIGNER FASHION

A warning, in memory of Annabel Hayling,
Whose designer laces were designed to be trailing.
When tied in a bow, as young Annabel said,
The expensive wording just couldn't be read.
Her parents pleaded that Annabel tie them,
But Annabel, foolishly, chose to defy them.
To all who, like her, might disregard warnings
In favour of fashion on dark winter mornings,
Beware of steep stairways and designer crazes,
Remember poor Annabel. DO UP YOUR LACES!

MRS MATILDA MOP

Mrs Matilda Mop
Fell asleep one day in a shop.
She awoke with a sneeze
And sat down on the peas
And the pods all started to POP!   to POP

                    to POP
                                    to POP
to POP

        to POP   **TO POP!**

As long as we have ... Feelings

GROWING UP

I don't want to grow up,
With legs that won't swing
When I sit on a bench,
Like my Dad.

And who wants to walk
When it's more fun to skip?
As people grow old
They grow sad.

I want to stand on my head
When the feeling comes on
And blow bubbles with gum
Till it pops.

I want to cry when things hurt me,
To be cuddled and held,
And to know that
The loving won't stop.

I don't want to grow up,
But everyone does,
As the years pass
I'm getting quite tall.

And though my legs soon won't swing
On the bench,
The good thing is
I now can see over the wall!

TWO ONTO ONE

Rachel's not friends with me.
She says that I smell.
She's poisoned Rebecca against me as well.
They won't share my hymn book,
Or help mix the paint.
They say if I'm near them
They both want to faint.
They're whispering about me
They giggle and lie,
I know tears will spill out
If I open my eyes.
Why are they mean to me?
What have I done?
It never seems fair
When it's two onto one.

ESCAPE

In our garden there's a summer-house
Where I sometimes go
When I don't want to play
And I don't want to know
What anyone else is doing.
I want to be by myself
And think.

I sit on the floor or the garden chair,
And don't do anything,
But think and stare,
And imagine a different world
Existing in there,
Just mine.

I don't want people to come and see,
I stay and dream quite happily.
It's peaceful and safe with only me,
No-one to argue and no-one to fight,
There in my own world, out of sight,
In the summer-house in our garden.

PAPER PEOPLE

I have some secret, special friends
Who always want to play
My games with me, and by my rules,
Who never run away.

They never disagree or fight,
They never sulk or shout,
They never say they will, then don't,
They never leave me out.

They are cut-out Paper People,
Coloured black and white and red,
They mostly sleep in silence
In a shoe-box by the bed.

But sometimes, when I'm on my own,
On jagged, broken days,
The box becomes my secret world,
And Paper People play.

WHERE WILL I BE TODAY?

Where will I be today?
Which bed will I sleep in tonight?
I know that both of them love me,
It's just each other they fight.

I can't seem to remember my lunch box,
And it's games and music today,
If it's true that both of them love me
Why won't one let me *stay?*

In the dark I imagine the reasons
For the breaking in two of their dreams.
Perhaps they just *thought* they would love me,
And having children is not what it seems.

Did I cause the sadness and worry
That replaced all the laughter and fun?
How can they possibly love me
If that's what my growing has done?

Where will I be today?
Which bed will I sleep in tonight?
I'm not sure if anyone loves me
In this battle of each other's rights.

NOT STUPID

I'm eight
And I don't *think* I'm stupid,
But some things I can't understand.
Why, when I know that I'm trying so hard,
Does my pencil seem drunk in my hand?

I'm eight
And I don't *think* I'm stupid,
But reading just fills me with dread.
Why do the letters and words move around,
And their sounds get mixed up in my head?

I'm eight
And I don't *think* I'm stupid,
But spelling's confusing my brain.
Which clever person made rough rhyme with stuff?
And are those drops rein, reign or rain?

I'm eight
And I don't *think* I'm stupid,
But it hurts when I'm told I don't try.
I want to read and to write and to spell,
I want to so much, I could cry.

And sometimes I do.

THE WORST THING IN THE WORLD

The worst thing in the world
Is when we have to go shopping.
The worst thing about the worst thing in the world,
Is that when we *do* go shopping
There is always someone my mother knows
Who goes shopping at the same time,
And we always bump into her.
Sometimes by the sugar,
Sometimes by the organic broccoli,
Sometimes by the quilted toilet rolls,
(Twelve for the price of nine,
in Rose, Grape, Snowflake, Buttercup and Blueberry)
But it always happens, without fail.
And then they talk, they talk, they talk.
And we wait, we wait, we wait.
We might wander around for a while,
Trying to take an interest in the thrills of the supermarket,
Trying not to poke holes in the sugar bags,
Or rub the seedy bits off the broccoli,
Or demolish the toilet roll mountain.
Hoping that whoever she meets
Will have laryngitis and can't talk,
Or diarrhoea and have to dash.
Longing for the day everyone shops on the Internet,
So that holidays and Saturdays
Won't always be ruined
By the worst thing in the world.

BETRAYAL

He told.

I'd wanted to be his friend
And sit next to him at the back.
I'd stuck up for him when things went wrong,
And said *I'd* caused the window to crack.

And he told.

The fun we had when I played the trick,
The pong as the stink bomb fell.
The holding of noses, the coughs and the groans,
The drama of seeming unwell.

And he told her.

Miss Matlock, our teacher, could not see the joke,
She spoke sternly of asthma and danger,
She demanded the name of the culprit,
And then, I saw that my "friend" was a stranger.

He told her

        it

            was

                ME.

He *told* her.

COPYCATS

I like her, I like her not.
We're best of friends, I hate her.
I'm turned to ice or furnace-hot
By my annoying imitator.

We laugh and whisper secrets,
But then she makes me mad,
When everything I choose or buy
She gets! (Or else she's had!)

"You know that dress you bought last week,
You'd been saving for so long?
I told my Dad how nice you looked –
Guess what? Now I've got one!"

It's dresses, CDs, songs and crisps,
It's everything that makes *me*.
When I turn to look at her
My reflection's what I see.

Do you know anyone like her?
Does your friend do it too?
If you have found the cure for this,
Please, may I copy you?

NIGHTMARE RECIPE

Mix a nightmare
Stir a nightmare
Pour in all your fears,
Add a shake of darkness
And several drops of tears.

Ingredients

- Creaking stairs and floorboards
  When you're all alone.
- The monster of the fireplace
  Who watches from the stone.
- The unseen angry creature
  Who whistles round the house.
- The scurrying night-time footsteps
  You're just hoping is a mouse!
- Skeletons and tree roots,
  Cobwebs in your hair.
- Torches without batteries
  And a dead fish stare.

Mix it well, your nightmare
Then throw it all away.
Wash it up, your mixing bowl
Ready for the day!

STARS

Twinkle, twinkle,
You're a star!

Stars have times when they shine brightly,
When they twinkle, and lighten the way
For people searching through the darkness,
Trying to find the way home.
Stars are good at shining and twinkling,
On the whole.

But sometimes it's hard to see stars.
Sometimes clouds form and swirl,
Hiding all but the occasional twinkle
In the gathering greyness.
Or a mist, light at first, deepens
Into a heavy blanket of fog
That makes the stars invisible.

But they are still there, and they are still stars.
And one day they will shine brightly again.

So twinkle, twinkle,
You're a star.

21

THE HUG RAP

I waken in the morning
And to start the day off well,
I need a hug for breakfast
And a hug goodbye as well,
As I set off for the classroom
With the friends from down the street.
And as I go I hug the dog
Plus everyone I meet.
I'm a huggy kind of person,
Just in case you want to know,
I hug in summer, autumn, spring
And twice as much in snow!
So if you see me coming
Spread your arms wide as the sea,
And fill the world with happiness
By HUGGING HUGGY ME!

THOUGHT DETECTIVE

Just because you *think* a thing
Doesn't mean it's true.
A thought is not a fact,
(Although they're good at tricking you.)
If you keep on thinking that
You're stupid, weak or plain,
In time you might believe it,
Giving thought the power of pain.

Become a Thought Detective,
Ask some questions, check and see
"Just where's the evidence for all
These charges against me?
I read and write, my muscles work,
My face won't shock the nation."
So catch those thoughts, consider them,
And keep them on probation.

LETTER TO STTTYO

1st Bedroom on the left
Top of the Stairs
Safe Haven

The Day It Happened

Chairman
Society for the Termination of theTorture of Ten-Year-Olds (S.T.T.T Y.O)
The World Out There That Needs To Know

Dear Sir or Madam,

I am regularly tortured. It's a story I must tell. Every month, without fail,
I'm dragged unwillingly to ——————————————well, you know where.

No-one asks me what I'd like, or *if* I'll come along. They just decide,
and make me go. They win because they're strong. Through the door
I'm hustled, to where the pain begins. With mirrors, lights and plastic
cloak fixed underneath my chin. Why don't they do it quickly? But that
would be too kind! Instead, they discuss, loudly, my oddness from
behind. They fetch apprentice torturers to observe the way they work,
while their instruments of agony snip and pull and jerk.

When they've had me at their mercy for what seems like half a year, they
end their fun with razors buzzing close behind my ear. Just when I think
it's over - when there's nothing left to hurt - the itching punishment
begins, deep down inside my shirt!

But worse, much worse than all the rest, is walking into school. The
stares, the jeers, discovering that even friends are cruel. So do something to stop it! Send a message to the Queen! For I'm a torture victim
who must be heard, not seen ——- for at least another week!

Yours in hiding,

Sean T.O. Day

IMPOSTER

From the deep and darkest shadows,
From corners, nooks, beyond the light,
Comes the one I cannot welcome
As I lie awake at night.

His voice is in the whispering curtains,
In creaking stairs and strange, dull knocks,
His voice is whistling through the air vents,
In midnight shouts of ticking clocks.

His scent clings to the cloak of darkness,
His taste is in the salt of tears,
His looks will be the cast of nightmares,
Until I turn to face my fears.

As long as there is ...
School

IT'S THE FIRST DAY BACK AT SCHOOL

Brushed and polished, shining,
It's the first day back at school.
Everyone looks different,
Tidy and taller.
Almost like strangers after six weeks.
We line up outside our new classroom,
Jostling to be near the ones we'd like to sit with.
Hoping they will jostle to be near us.
Trying to be first in the line
So that we can choose the best table.
The dreaded Miss Mole appears,
Looking as thin and fierce and frightening
As we were told she was by last year's leavers.
Silence.
We walk in,
Then *rush* to sit where we think we won't be noticed
Or asked questions.
But Miss Mole has a Class Plan
And she moves us all around
To where she can see us.
She asks us *lots* of questions.
The classroom feels alien.
It smells of pine polish and disinfectant
Instead of chalk and damp clothes and sweaty bodies,
Like classrooms should.
And the toilets don't smell at all.
It isn't normal.
It's the first day back at school.
Tomorrow will be better.

TIME

School time
Assembly time
Work time
Friendly time
Play time
Dinner time
Games time
Fun.

Reading time
Painting time
All the class
Is waiting time
Story time
Favourite time
School's all
Done.

FINDING FRIENDS

I want to be friends
I want to be friends
I want to be friends
I do.
I'll give you my sweets,
I'll lend you my pen
If I can be friends with you.
We'll sit side by side,
You can copy my work,
I'll let you go first into dinner.
You can plait my hair
At story time
And on Sport's Day
I'll let you be winner.
Please be my friend
As I'm new to this school
And nobody likes me I know,
I don't want to cry,
But my eyes feel all hot
And my feet are just wanting to go!

I can come to your house —————-
Your Mum won't mind at all,
I can stay till it's bedtime, you say —————-
So you *will* be my friend,
You're new here as well —————-
Then it hasn't been such a bad day!

MARCH MADNESS

A normal day,
A school day in March.
No problems are forecast at all.
The pupils seem normal
And in their right minds ————
Till a door's heard to bang in the hall.

Then, stealthily, sneakily,
No-one knows how,
Changes occur in the school.
A restlessness stirs,
And then simmers and spreads.
An infection that kills all the rules.

A spirit of wildness
Is loose in our midst.
Behaviour leaps out of control.
Playtime is Fight-time,
Fall-out-time and Cry-time,
Teachers are on police patrol.

The banging of back doors,
The tangling of trees,
The rubbish that's tossed through the air
Prepare those who *know*
How the rise of the wind
Causes madness, to those in their care.

THE BATTLE

The battle went on for weeks,
For months, for almost a year.
Many of us started the campaign,
Faced our enemy and our fear.

We struggled, we fought
The panic and the danger.
Some surrendered, joined the other side
We, who had shared, became strangers.

Our numbers dwindled with each skirmish,
Until there was only me,
Thrashing and kicking and battling for breath
In eye-stinging misery.

A leaning out and a letting go,
The thrill as the battle ended,
The enemy caught and held me safe,
I found myself befriended
As I swam.

RECIPE FOR PLAYTIME

Ingredients:

1 bell
6 carefully selected friends (to mix with)
2 to be left out (as they might spoil the mixture.)
15 teacher-free minutes
1 handful of ideas
Mixed fruit, sweets or crisps (for sharing)
Noise to taste.

Method:

1   Look at the clock when working.

2   Wait for the bell to ring.

3   Dash to your favourite tree trunk.

4   Hide from your friends , then S P R I N G!

5   Roll down the hill in freedom.

6   Decide who'll be on for tig.

7   Shout for your favourite leader.

8   Stand on your head, then dig!

9   Do all the things you want to,

10 Instead of the things they say.

11 Enjoy all the thrills of playtime,

12 And turn out for more next day!

This recipe should be used 3 times daily in order to ensure freshness.

YESTERDAY IT HAPPENED

After weeks of widths and armbands,
After a lifetime of "Long legs" and floats,
After terms and terms of trying so hard,
And gallons of pool up my nose,
Yesterday it happened.

I pushed off
And kicked and pulled;

Pushed off
And kicked and pulled;

Pushed off
And kicked and pulled;

Pushed off
And kicked and pulled
And kicked and pulled
And kicked and pulled
And kicked and pulled
And kicked and pulled
I SWAM.

And I'll never forget the feeling.

FIRST NIGHT AWAY

It's bedtime
The first night,
I wish I hadn't come.

Shifting shapes
And shadows,
I wish I could go home.

No-one else
Seems nervous,
I'm sure they're all asleep.

A thousand
Ghostly footsteps,
Are making my flesh creep.

Shivering
Beneath the sheets
I sense an evil beast.

It pounces
And it drags me out————
"Come share the midnight feast!"

PICK-AND-MIX PLAYTIME

Pick a friend, your best friend,
Pick a few more.
Wait for the bell to ring
Then *dash* through the door.
Mix up ideas
For things you can play,
Shout! Argue! Then pick out
The game for today.
Pick the place to play it,
Away from the rest,
A Pick-and-Mix playtime,
A great time ——*the best!*

TO SLIDE, OR NOT TO SLIDE?

Ice in the playground
Iron hard.
Playtimes of polishing
The slide down the yard
Mean danger and thrills
For those who will dare,
Mean wishing and wondering
For those who just stare.

Could I, would I
Be one of the few, who,
With hearts and lungs straining
Step into the queue?
I want to, I'm going to!
My moment's at hand...........then,
A shout from the staff-room,

"Sliding is BANNED!"

THE LEAVER

I'm in a strange place.

The sounds of security,
Voices, bells, echoes;
The days' patterns,
Familiar as breathing;
People who have made my world mine,
Who know when I'm happy
Or cross or upset
Don't belong to me any more.

I'm in a strange place.

I'm in a strange place.

Unable to reach out yet to the future.
Not sure I want the promised,
Exciting world of tomorrow.
Moving from the safe pond
I thought I'd outgrown,
To an ocean full of unknown swimmers
Which time says I must join.
But I don't belong to them yet.

I'm in a strange place.

THE FAMILIAR GNOMES OF MR JONES

There's a garden round the cottage
That belongs to Mr Jones,
It's an overcrowded garden
Full of strange, familiar stones.
There are wild, mysterious rumours
About Offsted's last inspection,
When several Year Six rebels
Disappeared without detection.
Mr Jones was seen to potter,
After school, around his garden
Placing newly sculptured statues
Before leaving them to harden.
A talented, artistic man
Who takes his school-work home,
Mr Jones plans peaceful lessons,
Undisturbed by garden gnomes.

As long as there are ...
Trees and other interesting things

WHERE SHALL WE GO FOR OUR HOLIDAYS?

As long as there are trees,
I don't mind where we go,
To Mablethorpe or to the moon,
Or Alaska in the snow.
All holidays are magical
Near mountains, lakes or seas,
Each place a perfect playground,
As long as there are trees.

As long as there are trees,
With branches gnarled and twisted,
Their fascination works on me
And cannot be resisted.
I have this strange compulsion,
Like a recurring disease,
It spreads through arms and legs, to brain,
I *have* to climb up trees.

As long as there are trees
I can make the world my own.
I climb and perch, the master of
My time-free travel zone.
No-one knows I'm out in space,
Or surviving treacherous seas,
Exploring all the universe————-
They think I'm climbing trees!

RED SQUIRRELS

They said they'd seen red squirrels,
The people we passed on the way up.
It was steep and rough and my legs ached
Long before the climb was done.
The climb to see the waterfall.
Seventy feet of tumbling, roaring water.
It would be good to have a picture of me
Being brave near the edge.
But I'd *rather* see red squirrels.

We met more people who said they'd seen them
High up amongst the trees.
Not the common, greedy, grey invaders
But *red* squirrels.
We'd see for ourselves, they said.
But we didn't.
We reached the waterfall sticky and tired.
We stood and admired it for what seemed like hours.
At last we began the trek down through the woodland.
Surely we'd spot them this time.
Stumbling over roots, I scanned the trees.
But nothing - no movement, no glint of red fur.
We saw cases from beech nuts cracked open and empty,
Oak trees and pine trees galore.
We saw long, ash-black slugs and fat, jet-black beetles.
We videoed rare butterflies.
But *I* wanted to see red squirrels.

We were almost down to the easy path when,
There before us, on the ground, we saw him.
Camouflaged by crisp, brown leaves and fading bracken,
Confident and poised, he held the stage,
Then darted off - a flash of rusty brightness.
Small and beautiful and belonging to this woodland.
And we had seen him.
Like getting a six to start a board game
Now we'd done it once, it was easy.
Three times we spotted him before he vanished.
Warm and flushed with success we reached the bottom,
Passing some people who were starting the climb.
"Have a good climb" we encouraged, "By the way——
We've seen red squirrels ...."

STONE SECRETS

Gnawing northern wind
Whips the wild waves to battle,
Crashing on the curtain wall,
The castle's only foe.
Unlikely landward raiders
Are two fields of chewing cattle,
Lifting heavy heads to watch
The curious come and go.

Rising through the moving mist,
The gatehouse and the tower
Guard centuries of secrets,
Solid stillness keeps them yet.
Stones which soaked up fear and fun,
Laughter, lust for power;
Stones, which shared the lives
Of generations, don't forget.

The air is full of certainty
Of walking over history;
Of breathing and of feeling
Just as others breathed and felt.
The stones, aloof with wisdom
Throw no light upon the mystery,
All feelings, thoughts and questions
In their watching presence melt.

POPPY

Dancing, twirling,
Cheerful, bright,
Lifts her face
In new delight.
Smiling, waving,
Giving pleasure,
A scarlet-coated
Dark-eyed treasure,
POPPY

RIVER REBELLION

For years we've been obedient,
Meandering where we belong,
Surrendering to work and pleasure,
Co-operative, though always strong.

Changes in the global climate,
Changes brought about by man
Bring changes in our moods and habits,
Let them control us now who can!

Rising, roaring, flowing faster,
Reaching higher, bursting free,
Flooding fields and homes and gardens,
Destroying lives relentlessly.

Once released we have no mercy,
Powerful in cruel play,
Mighty rivers in rebellion
Challenge mankind's selfish way.

Listen to the rivers' story
That warns you now of times ahead,
Respect us and respect the planet,
Remember what the rivers said.

As long as there are ... Families

MUMS TALK

Babies gurgle,
Boys shout,
Girls giggle,
Men call out,
But Mums talk.

Outside schools,
Inside shops,
On the 'phone
Which never stops,
Mums talk.

Children wait,
Husbands frown,
Teachers sigh,
Dogs sit down
While Mums talk.

Weather, old folks,
Cost of shoes,
Measles, mumps,
Village news,
Mums talk.

Morning, evening,
Noon and night,
Bathtime, bedtime
Then she *might*————————-stop.

(Or she *might*———————— talk in her sleep!)

JOB DESCRIPTION

A very special person
For a very special post.
Someone who knows how to cook,
(Especially beans on toast),
Someone who can clean the house
And drive children to school,
And buy the food and clothes and shoes
And use most household tools.
A teacher of all subjects,
A referee of fights,
Who, as relief from boredom,
Is an "on call" nurse at night.
A hairdresser and swimming coach,
At ease with dogs and cats,
(And hamsters, rabbits, fish and snakes,
Stick insects, birds and rats.)
Has laundry skills, a taxi cab,
Makes costumes for school plays.
Who *never* goes off duty
And whom no one *ever* pays.

HAIR PUZZLE

As Dads grow old, their heads can change,
Almost without them knowing.
Ben's Dad's hair is turning grey,
My Dad's got tired of growing.

And as Dad's hair receded
And grew really, really thin,
It slowly did a U-turn
And sprouted thickly on his chin.

So now his head top's shiny,
And his beard is long and thick,
Which is lovely while he's fit and well,
But awful when he's sick!

It puzzles Ben who's only three,
He asked me with a frown,
"Johnny, why's your Daddy's head
Been put on upside down? "

TIMMY WATSON

Timmy Watson killed our blackbirds,
He threw them by the shed.
A family of blackbirds,
Now everyone is dead.

He used to come and stalk them,
We chased him off each day.
But once when everyone was out
Those blackbirds had to pay.

My brothers said they'd kill him,
And show him how it felt
To be hunted and then murdered,
They planned to use Dan's belt.

But I said it was instinct.
You can't blame him for that.
It's sad about the blackbirds,
But Timmy Watson's just a cat!

BEING ROCKED

When I was small
I liked to be rocked
And cuddled up
Safe after tea.
My mother would sing to me
Songs she'd made up
About how there was room on her knee.
Her old rocking chair had rocked others before,
And my brother came after, but he
Wasn't there then,
That was my time alone,
Being rocked, by my Mum, on her knee.

WHAT IS IT WITH PARENTS AND HAIR?

No
No
No
I want it to grow.

You're having it cut anyway.

But
But
But
I must get it cut.

And look like a convict? No way!

What is it with parents and hair?

GRANDAD'S GREENHOUSE

When I stay with Grandad
He says "Now come with me"
And takes me to the greenhouse
Down the garden, past the tree.
It's the magic world of Grandad,
Full of pots, and plants all growing,
Watering cans and spades and hoes,
Soil, and seeds for sowing,

In Grandad's greenhouse.

Between the plants he has a chair
Where he can sit and think,
Or read his newspaper or sing,
Or rest to have his drink.
A different world of quietness,
It looks and smells, well - *green*,
We plant and weed till Grandma calls,
And *she* knows where we've been.......

In Grandad's greenhouse.

LIFE IS A CIRCLE

Soft, chubby face,
Finely sprinkled hair,
Sweet, pink-gum smile
Revealing odd, white milestones.
Sleeping, waking randomly,
No timetable.
Eating soft foods only.
Repeating familiar sounds,
Enjoying favourite stories
Again and again and again.
Dreams and daydreams
Drift into dozing.
Needing love,
Giving love.
Helpless becoming strong,
Strong becoming helpless.

Life is a circle.

As long as there are ...
Animals

JACK

Jack
is my best friend,
I know I can trust him.
I don't have to win things
or prove that I'm strong.
When I'm in trouble
and nobody likes me,
I just call for Jack –
he's for *me*, right or wrong.

Jack
is my best friend,
who shares all my secrets.
My partner for ball games
and jumping off beds.
The last one I see
as I drift into sleeping,
and just as the pictures
of night fill my head ——

Jack licks my nose.

SNAKES DON'T SMELL

Dogs? ——- No.
Jumping, bouncing
Through the park,
Hungry, hairy,
Dogs bark.

Snakes don't bark.

Hamsters? ——- No.
Sleeping day-times
Hidden well,
Noisy night-times,
Hamsters smell.

Snakes don't smell.

Rabbits? ——- No.
Scrabbling, twitching,
Dwarf or big,
In park or garden,
Rabbits dig.

Snakes don't dig.

Cats? ——- No.
Prowling, stalking
Birds to catch,
However friendly,
Cats scratch.

Snakes don't scratch.

No to dogs and cats and hamsters,
No to rabbits' mess.
Snakes are quiet, clean and charming,
So choose a snake,
Say Yessssssssssssssssssssssssssssss s s

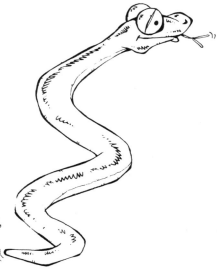

57

SEND FOR THE SNAKES

Floors needing polish,
Floors needing sheen,
Floors thick with mud and grime
Needing a clean?
Send for the experts,
A 'phone call it takes,
Send for the polishers,
Send for the Snakes.

Sidewinder, Python,
Cobra or Corn –
Naturally gifted
From the time they were born.

Slithering, sliding
Forwards and back,
Buffing and shining
Their reptilian track.
So walk all the mud in,
Spill juice and cakes,
Then send for the polishers
Send for the Snakes.

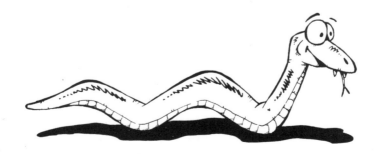

THE LADYBIRD DESIGNERS

Morning-wear, evening-wear,
To keep you cool or hot,
We'll design you anything
So long as it has spots.
We're the Ladybird Designers
"Tailor-made" or "Off the Shelf"
Satisfaction guaranteed
By Lady Bird herself.
She oversees the business,
Adding glamour to each day
As she floats about the workshop
In her scarlet negligee.
Choose your style, choose your silk,
Chiffon or even plastic,
Yellow, red or subtle brown
We'll make you look fantastic.
And when you have decided
How many spots to try,
We'll dress you up and push you off,
We know you'll want to fly!
For we're the Ladybird Designers,
Quite the top of our profession,
And ruthless to our rivals,
"Aphid House" and "Greenfly Mansion"

ROCKING RABBITS

I was walking in the moonlight,
I was walking through the wood,
When I saw the strangest sort of sight
A person ever could.
There were rabbits in the clearing
There were rabbits round the trees
There were rocking, rapping rabbits,
Twitching noses in the breeze.

There were rabbits from the pet shops,
From the gardens, from the moors,
There were rabbits used to hutches,
There were those who lived outdoors.
There were black and white and grey and brown,
With spots and patches too,
There were dwarf and large, with ears that trailed,
And rabbits meant for stew.

They were rocking, they were rolling,
They were leaping high as kites
On this
Hippy, hoppy,
Flippy, floppy,

Rocking Rabbit Rave-up Night.

ADELAIDE IDA

Adelaide Ida the dancing spider
Dances in the morning
With the sun beside her,
Dances in the evening
As the shadows hide her
Dancing, d
     a
       n
         g
         l
         i
        n
        g
    Adelaide Ida.

OUR HAMSTER PATCHES

Here lie the bones
Of our hamster, Patches,
Who left this earth
Whilst nibbling matches.
He took great delight
In chewing and churning,
Till he chewed the brimstone,
Which left his fur burning.
So lock up your hamsters,
Remember poor Patches,
And if you must light things,
Well, use *safety* matches.

DINAH

Dinah thumps and trundles,
Dinah stamps and shakes,
Dinah speaks like thunder,
Dinah makes earthquakes,
Dinah scares the children,
Dinah rocks and roars,
Dinah leaps from mountains
Then guess what.............
Dinah soars!

As long as there is ...
Word play

GUESS WHO HAIKU (5.7.5 SYLLABLES)

Neck which stretches high,
Patchwork skin in brown and gold,
A strange sight running.

Arachnid by name,
Enemy to careless flies,
Known to persevere.

Small furry mammal,
Long, radar ears, twitching nose,
Often called Peter.

Uninvited guests,
Small, scurrying night raiders,
Addicted to cheese.

(Mice)

(Rabbit)

(Spider)

(Giraffe)

CINQUAIN. (2.4.6.8.2 SYLLABLES)

Rock pool
Playground for crabs
Lucky dip for children
Hiders, seekers, losers, weepers,
Rock pool

TANKA.(5.7.5.7.7 SYLLABLES)

Entertainers

Diving, leaping high,
Performing grey clowns frolic
In bottle-nosed fun,
Entertaining the fish world,
Smiling sea stars, the dolphins.

FOX AND FROG KENNINGS

Wild howler
Night prowler
Free mealer
Chicken stealer
Earth liver
Fright giver
Rusty splasher
Hunted dasher
Fox.

Blobby maybe
Jelly baby
Black wriggler
Comma squiggler
Legs growing
Tail going
Pond plopper
Land hopper
Frog

X – ALONE

In the middle,
At the end,
Never on my own.
Always following,
That's me,
Except in Xylophone.
In *that* word
I line up first.
But even though I've led,
I'm not allowed
To make *my* sound .....
I have to sound like Z!

X IS THE NAME

Here are the surnames of the children in Club X. In order to be a member your first name must begin with "X". Try calling the register of members.

_____Act

_____Amine

_____Ample

_____Asperate

_____Change

_____Claim

_____Cuse

_____Ecute

_____Ercise

_____Ert

_____Ist

_____It

_____Plain

_____Plode

_____Ray

_____Terminate

Do you know anyone who could join this club?

FOOTBALL OUT-OF- FOCUS

NEWSFLASH...............
NEWSFLASH.................
NEWSFLASH.....

Good afternoon. Welcome to Football Out-of-Focus. This is Dennis Linehamup reporting.

We have just received this newsflash. Within the last half hour the teams have been announced for the annual Nouns v Verbs Football Final. However the selectors are not quite sure about the suitability of some of those selected and would welcome suggestions for substitutes. Here are the provisional selections:

Noun Namers		**Verb Action United**	
I	A. Ball	I	W.E. Kick
2	N.U. Strip	2	I. Swear
3	R. Fans	3	U. Shout
4	F. Lags	4	H. E. Dives
5	F.A. Cup	5	M. O. Wins
6	X. I. Players	6	Will Dribble
7	W. E. R. Best-Team	7	S. Hoots
8	K. Ickoff	8	C. M. Score
9	R. Penalty	9	U. R. Fouling
10	L. Ines- Man	10	R. Gue
11	R.E Feree	11	S.U. P. Porting

Please feel free to make your own selection of players and send them to:
Fooball Out-Of- Focus
c/o The Person In Charge
Wherever You Are
FUT BAII.

THE SCHOOL OF FISH

Here is our new school brochure with information about staff and activities.

Mr Shark Hammer	-	Head
Sir Dean Sandwich	-	Governor

Administrative Staff

Mr S Quids	-	Bursar
Mrs D Scales	-	Cook
Mrs Cuttle-Ree	-	Dinner supervisor

Teaching staff

Mr Bass	-	Music
Mr C Shanty		Singing (cheerful)
Mr WE Whale	-	Singing (mournful)
Mr Tuna	-	Piano
Miss Dab	-	Art
Miss P Laice	-	Craft
Mrs Weaver	-	Craft
Mr Mussel	-	PE
Mrs Sole	-	RE
Miss Conga	-	Dancing
Miss Ling	-	Chinese

The following prizes have been awarded:

Prize for achievement:	Star Fish
Prize for behaviour:	Angel Fish
Prize for modern music:	Rock Salmon
Prize for sponsored silence:	Hermit Crab
Prize for grooming:	Razor Fish
Prize for fencing:	Sword Fish

School Clubs:

Skating Club
Debaiting Club
Mountaineeling Club
Diving Club (See A.Pike)

School Rules:

Strictly NO SMOKING (By order of Professors Kipper, Salmon and Haddock.)
Avoid smoke-filled rooms.
Beware of the Internet
Line dancing is not encouraged
—if you do take part, avoid getting hooked.

School Pets:

Octo Puss and Dog Fish
(Known as Woof)

As long as there are ...
Seasons

EASTER THEN AND NOW

Jesus was a good man who said he was God.
Jesus was a good man who said he was God,
But bad things happened to him.

People followed him and wanted to be near him.
People followed him and wanted to be near him,
Then turned against him.

His friends promised to stand by him.
His friends promised to stand by him,
Then deserted him when he needed them most.

One friend looked after the money.
One friend looked after the money,
Then betrayed his secret to his enemies for thirty pieces of silver.

Crowds welcomed him one day and shouted "Hosanna."
Crowds welcomed him one day and shouted "Hosanna,"
Then shouted "Crucify him," a few days later.

Bystanders watched him suffer.
Bystanders watched him suffer and didn't try to help him.

Jesus died.
Jesus died and three days later he came alive again.

Jesus was a good man who said he was God.
Jesus was a good man who said he was God,
But bad things happened to him.

Bad things still happen.
Bad things still happen to good people.

People turn against friends.
People turn against friends and desert them.
People turn against friends and desert them and betray secrets.
People turn against friends and desert them and betray secrets
And say different things on different days.
People turn against friends and desert them and betray secrets
And say different things on different days
And watch them suffer without trying to help.

But Jesus, who said he was God, died.
But Jesus, who said he was God, died
And three days later he came alive again.

He knows what it's like.
He knows what it's like and never deserts, or betrays secrets,
Or changes what he says, or watches without helping.

Jesus was a good man.
Jesus was a good man, who said he was God.

FIRE

Blazing trees
Throw off sparks
That huddle in heaps on the ground.
Gusts re-ignite a fleeting protest,
Feet stir fading embers
As the year dies
In the fire of autumn.

HARVEST CODE AND QUESTIONS

H	A	R	V	E	S	T
1	2	3	4	5	6	7

If the world would	6 1 2 3 5
Fewer people would	6 7 2 3 4 5
More people could	5 2 7
If the world would	1 5 2 3
Those who	1 2 4 5
Could	6 2 4 5
The	3 5 6 7
Where are our	7 5 2 3 6
When the world won't	6 1 2 3 5 ?
Where is our	1 5 2 3 7 ?

77

NOVEMBER NEEDS DRAGONS

Early darkness,
Dreary days,
Drizzling dampness
Like clingfilm.
Greyness gathers
Into weeks,
Punctured once
As dragon's breath
Exhaled, multiplies
A million sparklets
Across the kingdom,
Five days into the gloom
Which is November.

WE WILL REMEMBER SOME OF THEM

Every year they sell poppies at our school.
Someone goes round all the classes with a tray.
Single poppies
Double poppies
Sprays of poppies,
Huge poppies for cars,
And best of all poppies on wooden crosses.
Like swords.
No-one's allowed to buy those
Because one year Peter Potts got two for a pound
And fought a duel with Billy Watson.
Our head said it was disrespectful
And banned them.

They're to remind us of the wars
And the men who died.
They do it every year so that we'll never forget
The eleventh hour of
The eleventh day of
The eleventh month,
When the fighting stopped,
But the crying and the dying didn't.

My Great-grandad was in
The Second World War.
He was a footballer before he had to go.
He didn't want to be a soldier.
He didn't want to go, but he had to.
Had to leave his wife, his baby and the team.
He was too old to play when the war ended,
So he sold bread and never had holidays.
He came back.
He would have been eighty-three next birthday.
But last November was cold.
His fire was turned right down when
He died.
And every year they sell poppies.............

ANTICIPATION

It's half past four in the morning,
The cold air greets my nose.
With a shiver of excitement
I explore with my toes.
Is it too early? Has he been?
He might be in here still!
But the only thing that's moving
Is the sack he came to fill.
My feet explore the intriguing shapes
As I make the mystery last,
The year's most thrilling moments
Will soon be in the past.

BACK TO FRONT CHRISTMAS

There's something odd about Christmas,
In a back to front sort of way.
I can't help thinking that Christmas
Is a back to front sort of day.

We give presents to all of our family,
And people give presents to us,
But what have we done to deserve it
And why do we need such a fuss?

It's strange that the person whose birthday
Is the cause of this annual rave
Is often ignored, and not mentioned
On the cards and the presents we gave.

He's left out of his very own party,
No presents for Jesus today,
In the rush of our back to front Christmas
His presents are hidden away.

A thank you would be a good present
For the treasure the poor shepherds found,
Just a moment to think about Jesus
Turns our back to front Christmas back round.

CHRISTMAS CRIB

Eyes shine,
Faces alight
With wonder and hope
On this special night.

The stable, the figures,
The straw and the manger
Tell the story of homelessness,
Joy and of danger,
Of visits by angels,
By poor men and rich,
Of presents and ponderings,
Of God's love by which
Jesus was born
On a night, oh, so still.
Parents gaze with their children,
The scene speaks until

Eyes shine,
Faces alight
With wonder and hope
On this special night.

POEMS PREVIOUSLY PUBLISHED

Minibeasts, Brian Moses, Macmillan 1999 ISBN 033037057 X (*Ladybird Designers*)

Whizz Bang Orang Utan, John Foster, OUP 1999 ISBN0 19 276193 5 (*Mrs Matilda Mop*)

Football Fever, John Foster OUP 2000, ISBN 0 19 2762220 (*Football out of Focus*)

The Way Through the Woods, John Foster OUP 2000, ISBN 0 19 917285 4 (*Recipe for Playtime*)

The Mighty Ark, John Foster OUP 2000, ISBN 0 19 917284 6 (*Guess Who Haiku*)

I'm in a Mood Today, John Foster, OUP 2000 ISBN 0 19 276229 X (*Betrayal* and *Copycats*)

Firewords, John Foster OUP 2000, ISBN 0 19 276243 5 (*Guess Who Haiku*)

Welcome to the Snake Hotel, Brian Moses , Macmillan 2001, ISBN 0 330 48261 0 (*Send for the Snakes*)

Never Play Snap with a Shark, John Foster, Macmillan 2001, ISBN 0 330 39370 7 (*Epitaph to a Victim of Designer Fashion*)

Aliens Stole My Underpants 2, Brian Moses Macmillan (*Life in Alien Nation*), ISBN 0 330 483463

POEMS DUE TO BE PUBLISHED

Dangerous Dinosaurs, Brian Moses, Macmillan (*Duvetsaurus Featherfill* and *Dinah*)

Eccentric Epitaphs, Harper – Collins 2001, John Foster (*Epitaph to a Victim of Designer Fashion*)

The School Year: Poems from September to July Brian Moses, August 2001 (*Yesterday it happened*, *We will remember some of them* and *The first day back at school*)

Cock-a-Doodle Moo, John Foster OUP 2001 (*Grandad's Greenhouse* and *Adelaide Ida*)

Ready, Steady Rap, John Foster OUP 2001 (*Rocking Rabbits*)

Enjoyed this book? Then why not try...

BRILLIANT!

In Bernard Young's latest collection of poems for the young and young at heart, there are poems about behaving brilliantly and behaving badly! Poems about chocolate, robots and aliens. Exciting poems, funny poems, horrible poems. *Brilliant!* by Bernard Young. Illustrations by Tod Leedale

Price: £4.95   **ISBN 1 902039 08 4**

Sales

City Information Service
Hull Central Library,
Albion Street,
Kingston upon Hull
HU1 3TF
UK

Telephone: +44 (0)1482 223344
Fax: +44 (0)1482 616896
E-mail: city.information@hullcc.gov.uk

www.hullcc.gov.uk/kingstonpress  Kingston **Press**